The Joke Machine

Roderick Hunt   Alex Brychta

Characters

Wilf

Biff

Anneena

Chip

Nadim

Mrs May

Scene 1   In the playground

Wilf   I've got a good joke.
            What goes black, white, black, white,
            black, white?'

Biff   I don't know.

Wilf   A penguin rolling down a hill.

(Everyone laughs.)

Anneena   I've got one.

Why couldn't the skeleton go to the party?

Chip   Why couldn't the skeleton go to the party?

Anneena   It had nobody to go with. *(pause)* No body - get it?

(The whistle sounds.)

3

Mrs May	*(calling)* Time to come inside. Line up quietly, everyone.
Nadim	What do sea monsters eat? Fish and ships.
Biff	*(groans)* That's a terrible joke.
Mrs May	Come on, you chatterboxes. Didn't you hear the whistle?

Wilf   Sorry, Mrs May.
We were telling jokes.

Mrs May   Well it's time to stop, now.

Biff   Mrs May! What does an elephant do on
a motorway?

Mrs May   Not now, Biff.
Tell me later.
(calls)   In you go, everyone.

Nadim   *(whispers)*   Biff! What does an elephant do on a motorway?

Biff   About two miles an hour.

Nadim   Ha! Ha! Very funny.

Mrs May   Biff! Nadim! Go inside quietly.

Scene 2   In the classroom

Mrs May   Well done, everyone.
You have worked hard today.
Now it's time to tidy up.

(The children start to tidy up.)

Anneena   Mrs May. Do you want to hear one of
Nadim's jokes?

Mrs May	Well, just one.
	I want to get home tonight!
Nadim	Why do cows wear bells?
Mrs May	I don't know.
	Why do cows wear bells?
Nadim	Because their horns don't work.

(Mrs May groans.)

Biff   I don't get that one.

Mrs May   *(claps her hands)*   I want to ask you something.
Who knows about 'Help the Children' day?

Chip   There's a special day, once a year.

Wilf   People raise money to help children.

Mrs May   What could we do for 'Help the Children'?

Anneena   Maybe we could raise money.

Biff   That's a great idea.

Mrs May   Think about it.
Tomorrow you can tell me your ideas.

Scene 3   At Biff and Chip's house

Wilf   There must be something we can think of.

Chip   I can't think of anything.

Anneena   I can't think of anything, either.

Biff   What have we got so far?
              Read out the list, Nadim.

Nadim Ideas for 'Help the Children'.
One - washing cars.
Two - toy sale.

Anneena That's only two ideas.

Wilf Well, we've only had two ideas.

Chip I don't think washing cars is a good idea.

Biff　　No.
I don't think Mrs May would let us.

Wilf　　And I gave all my old toys to the last toy sale.

Nadim　　Hang on! I've had a brilliant idea.

Everyone　　What?

Nadim　　A joke machine.

Scene 4   At school the next day

Anneena   Mrs May! Mrs May! We've got a great
idea for 'Help the Children'.

Mrs May   It must be a good one.
You all sound excited.

Biff   It's a joke machine.

Chip	We write jokes on slips of paper.
	Then we put the jokes in a box.
Wilf	The box is the joke machine.
Anneena	It's a great idea.
	People pay for a joke.
Wilf	They give some money and
	they get a joke from the box.

Biff	Do you think it will work?
Mrs May	I think it's a lovely idea. But I can see one problem.
Everyone	What's that?
Mrs May	You will need lots and lots of jokes.

Scene 5   In the classroom

Biff   We have finished the joke machine.

Chip   It's brilliant.
Look! I've finished the poster.

Wilf   *(reads)*   A laugh does you good.
Do good with a laugh.

Nadim   We have put the jokes on the computer.

Anneena   Now we can print them off.

Nadim   Here's the next joke:
What game do horses play?

Anneena   Stable tennis.

Wilf   How many jokes have we got?

Nadim   Forty nine.
I wish we had some more.

Mrs May   Here is one more joke for you.

Biff   That will make it fifty.

Mrs May   What can fly and has four legs?

Everyone   We don't know.
What can fly and has four legs?

Mrs May   Two birds.

(Everyone laughs.)

Scene 6   In the shopping centre

Chip   Roll up! Roll up!

Wilf   Support 'Help the Children'.

Biff   Buy a joke.
             Not less than 50p.

Nadim   Here's somebody, now.

Chip   He's given us a pound.
            Thank you, Sir.

Anneena   He wants us to tell the joke.

Biff   Let's do it together.

Everyone   What has only one foot?
                (pause)
                A leg.

(Everyone laughs.)

Mrs May   I have some good news.
The mayor loves your joke machine.
She wants to buy all the jokes.

Biff   That's brilliant!

Mrs May   Guess how much she will pay for each
joke.

Everyone   We don't know.
How much will she pay for each joke?

Mrs May   Two pounds for each joke!

Nadim   Fifty jokes at two pounds each!
That's a hundred pounds.

Wilf   But we've sold twenty jokes.
There are only thirty left.

Nadim   No! I've been putting them back.
There are still fifty in there.

Anneena   Three cheers for Nadim.

Mrs May   Three cheers for the Joke Machine!

Nadim   I've thought of another joke.
What card game do crocodiles like?

Everyone   We don't know.
What card game do crocodiles like?

Nadim   Snap!

(Everyone groans.)